TARGET YOUR MATHS

Year 3

Practice Workbook

Elmwood Education

First published 2018 by
Elmwood Education
Unit 5
Mallow Park
Watchmead
Welwyn Garden City
Herts. AL7 1GX
Tel. 01707 333232

Reprinted 2019

ISBN 978 1906 622 664

Typeset and illustrated by Tech-Set Ltd., Gateshead, Tyne and Wear.
Cover illustrated by Stephen Hill
Email: hilly.moto@btinternet.com

PREFACE

Target your Maths Year 3 Practice Workbook has been written to accompany Target your Maths Year 3 Text Book. The Practice Workbook is intended to provide pupils with the material to consolidate their learning, whether used in the classroom or at home.

The structure of the Practice Workbook matches that of Appendix III found in Target your Maths Year 3 Answer Book. In Appendix III the Year 3 Programme of Study is organised into twelve termly blocks. In Appendix IV overleaf each page of the Practice Workbook is matched with the corresponding block and page(s) of Target your Maths Year 3 Text Book.

Whereas each lesson in Target your Maths Year 3 is pitched at three different ability levels, the Practice Workbook is based solely upon the requirements of Year 3 pupils, the ability level covered by Section B of Target your Maths.

The author is indebted to many colleagues who have assisted him in this work. He is particularly grateful to Sharon Granville and Davina Tunkel for their invaluable assistance and advice.

Stephen Pearce

APPENDIX IV

The references are for the blocks found in Appendix III of the Target your Maths Year 3 Answer Book and the page numbers in the Target your Maths Year 3 Text Book.

TERM 1		BLOCK	PAGE(s)
1	Numbers	1	2–3
2	Finding 10, 100 More/Less	1	8
3	Mental +/− (HTU +/− U)	2	12
4	Mental +/− (HTU +/− T, H)	2	13,14
5	Multiplication Facts for 3	3	34
6	Multiplying by Multiples of 10 (1)	3	40
7	Measuring Length 1	4	74–75
8	Presenting Data-Pictograms	5	118–119
9	Interpreting Pictograms	5	120–121
10	Written Method (+) 1	6	24
11	Written Method (−) 1	6	26
12	Multiplication Facts for 4	7	35
13	Dividing Multiples of 10 (1)	7	44
14	Reading The Time 1	8	88–89
15	Recognising Fractions	9	61
16	Drawing 2-D Shapes	10	105
17	2-D Shapes	10	108–109
18	Written Method (×) 1	11	46
19	Money	12	97,98
20	Measures Problems 1	12	102

TERM 2		BLOCK	PAGE(s)
21	Place Value and Partitioning	1	5
22	Counting in 1s, 10s, 100s	1	9
23	Written Method (+) 2	2	25
24	Written Method (−) 2	2	27
25	Multiplying by Multiples of 10 (2)	3	42
26	Dividing Multiples of 10 (2)	3	45
27	Metric Units	4	81
28	Presenting Data in Bar Charts	5	122–123
29	Mental +/− (Multiples of 10)	6	17
30	Addition Pyramids	6	32
31	Multiplication Facts for 8	7	37
32	Written Method (×) 2	7	47
33	Written Method (÷) 1	7	51
34	Measuring Length 2	8	76–77
35	Fractions of a Set	9	65

36	Equivalent Fractions	9	67
37	Angles	10	113
38	Division Problems	11	54
39	Mental +/− of Measures	12	83
40	Reading The Time 2	12	90–91

TERM 3		**BLOCK**	**PAGE(s)**
41	Place Value	1	6
42	Counting 4s, 8s, 50s, 100s	1	11
43	Mental +/−	2	18
44	Using Partitioning to +/−	2	23
45	Multiplication Facts Review	3	39
46	Written Method (÷) 2	3	52
47	Measuring Weight/Capacity	4	73
48	Measures Problems 2	4	101
49	Interpreting Bar Charts	5	126–127
50	Missing Number Problems (+/−)	6	30
51	Word Problems +/−	6	31
52	Written Method ×/÷	7	53
53	Word Problems ×/÷	7	57
54	Time Problems	8	96
55	+/− Fractions	9	70
56	Comparing Fractions	9	71
57	3-D Shapes	10	110–111
58	Angles in Shapes	10	114
59	Measures Problems ×/÷	11	104

REVIEW		**BLOCK**	**PAGE(s)**
60	Number Review	12	130
61	Mental Calculations Review	12	131
62	Written Calculations Review	12	131
63	Fractions Review	12	132
64	Measures Review	12	133
65	Year 3 Review	12	135

CONTENTS

TERM 1
1 Numbers
2 Finding 10, 100 More/Less
3 Mental +/− (HTU +/− U)
4 Mental +/− (HTU +/− T, H)
5 Multiplication Facts For 3
6 Multiplying by Multiples of 10 (1)
7 Measuring Length 1
8 Presenting Data-Pictograms
9 Interpreting Pictograms
10 Written Method (+) 1
11 Written Method (−) 1
12 Multiplication Facts For 4
13 Dividing Multiples of 10 (1)
14 Reading The Time 1
15 Recognising Fractions
16 Drawing 2-D Shapes
17 2-D Shapes
18 Written Method (×) 1
19 Money
20 Measures Problems 1

TERM 2
21 Place Value and Partitioning
22 Counting in 1s, 10s, 100s
23 Written Method (+) 2
24 Written Method (−) 2
25 Multiplying by Multiples of 10 (2)
26 Dividing Multiples of 10 (2)
27 Metric Units
28 Presenting Data-Bar Charts
29 Mental +/− (Multiples of 10)
30 Addition Pyramids
31 Multiplication Facts for 8
32 Written Method (×) 2
33 Written Method (÷) 1
34 Measuring Length 2
35 Fractions of a Set
36 Equivalent Fractions
37 Angles

38 Division Problems
39 Mental +/− of Measures
40 Reading The Time 2

TERM 3
41 Place Value
42 Counting 4s, 8s, 50s, 100s
43 Mental +/−
44 Using Partitioning to +/−
45 Multiplication Facts Review
46 Written Method (÷) 2
47 Measuring Weight/Capacity
48 Measures Problems 2
49 Interpreting Bar Charts
50 Missing Number Problems (+/−)
51 Word Problems +/−
52 Written Method ×/÷
53 Word Problems ×/÷
54 Time Problems
55 +/− Fractions
56 Comparing Fractions
57 3-D Shapes
58 Angles in Shapes
59 Measures Problems ×/÷

REVIEW
60 Number Review
61 Mental Calculations Review
62 Calculations Review
63 Fractions Review
64 Measures Review
65 Year 3 Review

Write these numbers in figures.

1 fifty-three ....

2 two hundred ....

3 seven hundred and thirty-one ....

4 one hundred and ninety-four ....

5 nine hundred and sixty-one ....

6 five hundred and twelve ....

7 six hundred and forty ....

8 three hundred and eighty-five ....

9 eight hundred and seven ....

10 one thousand ....

Write these numbers in words.

11 160 ....

12 532 ....

13 97 ....

14 358 ....

15 703 ....

16 481 ....

17 820 ....

18 919 ....

19 605 ....

20 574 ....

Work out

1 175 + 10   ....

2 803 + 10   ....

3 646 + 10   ....

4 328 + 10   ....

5 492 + 10   ....

6 260 − 10   ....

7 937 − 10   ....

8 509 − 10   ....

9 781 − 10   ....

10 614 − 10   ....

11 347 + 100   ....

12 695 + 100   ....

13 158 + 100   ....

14 524 + 100   ....

15 872 + 100   ....

16 419 − 100   ....

17 731 − 100   ....

18 186 − 100   ....

19 297 − 100   ....

20 563 − 100   ....

Write the missing number in the box.

21 [   ] + 10 = 925

22 [   ] + 10 = 128

23 [   ] + 10 = 762

24 [   ] + 10 = 241

25 [   ] + 10 = 307

26 [   ] − 10 = 650

27 [   ] − 10 = 583

28 [   ] − 10 = 816

29 [   ] − 10 = 439

30 [   ] − 10 = 794

31 [   ] + 100 = 917

32 [   ] + 100 = 384

33 [   ] + 100 = 625

34 [   ] + 100 = 1000

35 [   ] + 100 = 849

36 [   ] − 100 = 251

37 [   ] − 100 = 732

38 [   ] − 100 = 468

39 [   ] − 100 = 96

40 [   ] − 100 = 673

Examples	$7 + 5 = 12$	$13 - 9 = 4$
	$27 + 5 = 32$	$83 - 9 = 74$
	$427 + 5 = 432$	$783 - 9 = 774$

Work out

1 $427 + 4$ ....

2 $165 + 9$ ....

3 $318 + 5$ ....

4 $793 + 7$ ....

5 $595 - 6$ ....

6 $230 - 3$ ....

7 $844 - 8$ ....

8 $682 - 4$ ....

9 $364 + 8$ ....

10 $578 + 6$ ....

11 $856 + 7$ ....

12 $129 + 9$ ....

13 $981 - 5$ ....

14 $645 - 7$ ....

15 $712 - 6$ ....

16 $494 - 9$ ....

17 $726 + 5$ ....

18 $257 + 8$ ....

19 $199 + 4$ ....

20 $874 + 6$ ....

21 $500 - 8$ ....

22 $913 - 5$ ....

23 $486 - 9$ ....

24 $342 - 7$ ....

Find

25 5 more than 617 ....

26 4 less than 470 ....

27 8 more than 185 ....

28 6 less than 954 ....

29 4 more than 536 ....

30 9 less than 321 ....

31 7 more than 869 ....

32 5 less than 294 ....

33 6 more than 287 ....

34 8 less than 735 ....

35 9 more than 893 ....

36 7 less than 516 ....

37 7 more than 624 ....

38 5 less than 261 ....

39 4 more than 148 ....

40 4 less than 372 ....

Examples	86 + 40 = 126	419 − 70 = 349
	583 + 400 = 983	765 − 700 = 65

Work out

1 158 + 60 ....

2 472 + 90 ....

3 817 − 70 ....

4 349 − 90 ....

5 346 + 200 ....

6 295 + 500 ....

7 573 − 400 ....

8 961 − 200 ....

9 283 + 50 ....

10 695 + 80 ....

11 724 − 40 ....

12 136 − 60 ....

13 518 + 300 ....

14 320 + 600 ....

15 759 − 500 ....

16 834 − 300 ....

17 491 + 40 ....

18 753 + 70 ....

19 938 − 80 ....

20 194 − 30 ....

21 192 + 400 ....

22 647 + 300 ....

23 609 − 200 ....

24 924 − 600 ....

Find

25 70 more than 769 ....

26 90 less than 433 ....

27 60 more than 581 ....

28 40 less than 208 ....

29 500 more than 154 ....

30 400 less than 679 ....

31 300 more than 91 ....

32 200 less than 708 ....

33 90 more than 396 ....

34 30 less than 947 ....

35 80 more than 874 ....

36 60 less than 262 ....

37 400 more than 382 ....

38 300 less than 945 ....

39 200 more than 617 ....

40 500 less than 536 ....

Write the missing number in the box.

1 8 × 3 = ☐   **5** 10 × 3 = ☐   **9** 3 × 3 = ☐

2 5 × 3 = ☐   **6** 1 × 3 = ☐   **10** 7 × 3 = ☐

3 11 × 3 = ☐   **7** 9 × 3 = ☐   **11** 4 × 3 = ☐

4 2 × 3 = ☐   **8** 6 × 3 = ☐   **12** 12 × 3 = ☐

13 12 ÷ 3 = ☐   **17** 21 ÷ 3 = ☐   **21** 6 ÷ 3 = ☐

14 27 ÷ 3 = ☐   **18** 9 ÷ 3 = ☐   **22** 33 ÷ 3 = ☐

15 3 ÷ 3 = ☐   **19** 30 ÷ 3 = ☐   **23** 15 ÷ 3 = ☐

16 36 ÷ 3 = ☐   **20** 18 ÷ 3 = ☐   **24** 24 ÷ 3 = ☐

25 ☐ × 3 = 18   **29** ☐ × 3 = 24   **33** ☐ × 3 = 30

26 ☐ × 3 = 9   **30** ☐ × 3 = 6   **34** ☐ × 3 = 27

27 ☐ × 3 = 33   **31** ☐ × 3 = 36   **35** ☐ × 3 = 3

28 ☐ × 3 = 15   **32** ☐ × 3 = 12   **36** ☐ × 3 = 21

37 ☐ ÷ 3 = 7   **41** ☐ ÷ 3 = 9   **45** ☐ ÷ 3 = 4

38 ☐ ÷ 3 = 1   **42** ☐ ÷ 3 = 6   **46** ☐ ÷ 3 = 11

39 ☐ ÷ 3 = 5   **43** ☐ ÷ 3 = 10   **37** ☐ ÷ 3 = 2

40 ☐ ÷ 3 = 12   **44** ☐ ÷ 3 = 3   **48** ☐ ÷ 3 = 8

Fill in the boxes.

1 $6 \times 2 =$ ☐

$6 \times 20 =$ ☐

2 $4 \times 5 =$ ☐

$4 \times 50 =$ ☐

3 $11 \times 4 =$ ☐

$110 \times 4 =$ ☐

4 $7 \times 3 =$ ☐

$70 \times 3 =$ ☐

5 $7 \times 5 =$ ☐

$7 \times 50 =$ ☐

6 $12 \times 3 =$ ☐

$12 \times 30 =$ ☐

7 $3 \times 2 =$ ☐

$30 \times 2 =$ ☐

8 $8 \times 4 =$ ☐

$80 \times 4 =$ ☐

9 $5 \times 3 =$ ☐

$5 \times 30 =$ ☐

10 $6 \times 4 =$ ☐

$6 \times 40 =$ ☐

11 $9 \times 5 =$ ☐

$90 \times 5 =$ ☐

12 $11 \times 2 =$ ☐

$110 \times 2 =$ ☐

Write the answer only.

13 2×40 ....

14 9×20 ....

15 80×3 ....

16 120×5 ....

17 9×30 ....

18 12×40 ....

19 50×5 ....

20 70×2 ....

21 6×50 ....

22 12×20 ....

23 40×3 ....

24 50×4 ....

Fill in the boxes.

25 Six 20 g weights

Total weight is ☐

26 40 cans in each box

☐ cans in 5 boxes

27 30 children in each class

☐ children in 8 classes

28 120 ml in each glass

☐ ml in 6 glasses

29 Nine 50p coins

£ ☐ altogether

30 4 potatoes in one bag

☐ potatoes in 70 bags

Read the measurements shown on each ruler.

1

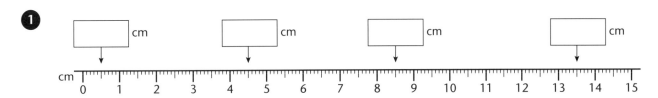

2

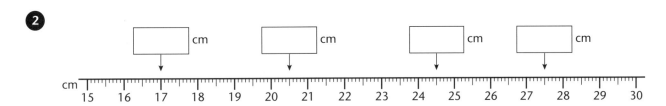

Measure these lines to the nearest half centimetre.

3 _____ [ ] cm

4 _____ [ ] cm

5 _____ [ ] cm

6 _____ [ ] cm

7 _____ [ ] cm

8 _____ [ ] cm

Measure the sides of each shape. Work out the perimeters.

9

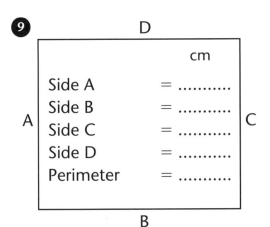

D

	cm
Side A	= ....
Side B	= ....
Side C	= ....
Side D	= ....
Perimeter	= ....

A ... C

B

10

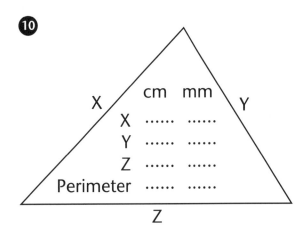

	cm	mm
X	......	......
Y	......	......
Z	......	......
Perimeter	......	......

X ... Y

Z

For each pictogram:

a) draw your symbol in the key

b) present the data shown in the table, drawing your symbols in neat rows and columns.

1 This table shows the number of dresses sold in a shop.

Key [ ] represents 10 dresses

Day	Dresses
Monday	30
Tuesday	40
Wednesday	70
Thursday	50
Friday	60
Saturday	80

Mon							
Tues							
Wed							
Thurs							
Fri							
Sat							

2 This table shows the flavour of lollies sold from an ice cream van.

Key [ ] represents 2 lollies

Flavour	Lollies
blackcurrant	4
lemon	6
orange	12
pineapple	16
raspberry	10
strawberry	14

b'currant							
lemon							
orange							
p'apple							
r'berry							
s'berry							

This pictogram shows the number of lengths of a pool swum by 5 children.

This pictogram shows the number of meals served in a restaurant.

 represents 2 lengths

Tuesday

Wednesday

Thursday

Friday

Saturday

represents 10 meals

1 How many lengths were swum by:

a) Ama   ....

b) Erin?   ....

2 Who swam:

a) 8 lengths   ....

b) 14 lengths?   ....

3 How many more lengths were
swum by Bob than Cath?   ....

4 How many fewer lengths were
swum by Dean than Erin?   ....

5 How many lengths were swum
by the 5 children altogether? ....

6 How many meals were served on:

a) Wednesday   ....

b) Friday?   ....

7 On which day were:

a) 50 meals served   ....

b) 20 meals served?   ....

8 How many fewer meals were
served on Thursday than Friday?   ....

9 How many more meals were served
on Wednesday than Tuesday?

....

10 How many meals were served
in the 5 days altogether?   ....

Examples

```
    5 9 3          6 4 6
  + 1 6 8        + 2 7 5
  -------        -------
    7 6 1          9 2 1
    1 1            1 1
```

Work out

1
```
    5 2 8
  + 1 5 4
  -------
```

2
```
    2 4 5
  + 1 9 3
  -------
```

3
```
    1 3 7
  + 1 2 5
  -------
```

4
```
    3 9 0
  + 3 6 6
  -------
```

5
```
    7 4 6
  + 2 4 7
  -------
```

6
```
    6 5 1
  + 1 8 5
  -------
```

7
```
    4 3 5
  + 3 9 5
  -------
```

8
```
    3 6 9
  + 1 5 4
  -------
```

9
```
    5 8 6
  + 1 7 9
  -------
```

10
```
    6 5 7
  + 2 4 8
  -------
```

11
```
    2 7 3
  + 2 4 0
  -------
```

12
```
    4 9 6
  + 4 8 4
  -------
```

13
```
    5 4 9
  + 2 7 2
  -------
```

14
```
    7 8 7
  + 1 5 3
  -------
```

15
```
    4 6 5
  + 2 8 9
  -------
```

16
```
    3 9 4
  + 2 1 6
  -------
```

17
```
    5 5 8
  + 1 6 9
  -------
```

18
```
    6 7 6
  + 3 9 6
  -------
```

Examples	$\overset{6}{\cancel{7}}\overset{1}{3}\;8$	$\overset{8}{\cancel{9}}\overset{11}{\cancel{2}}\overset{1}{3}$
	$-\quad 1\;6\;5$	$-\;5\;4\;8$
	$5\;7\;3$	$3\;7\;5$

Work out

1
```
   4 8 2
 - 3 3 9
 -------
```

2
```
   3 0 6
 - 1 2 3
 -------
```

3
```
   8 7 5
 - 6 4 8
 -------
```

4
```
   5 3 4
 - 2 7 3
 -------
```

5
```
   6 9 1
 - 4 5 7
 -------
```

6
```
   7 4 5
 - 3 6 5
 -------
```

7
```
   9 5 7
 - 7 6 2
 -------
```

8
```
   2 9 3
 - 2 4 5
 -------
```

9
```
   5 1 8
 - 1 4 4
 -------
```

10
```
   8 7 6
 - 3 5 8
 -------
```

11
```
   7 2 5
 - 5 7 9
 -------
```

12
```
   4 8 0
 - 1 2 7
 -------
```

13
```
   6 6 4
 - 3 0 8
 -------
```

14
```
   9 5 9
 - 4 7 6
 -------
```

15
```
   3 9 2
 - 2 1 3
 -------
```

16
```
   7 0 7
 - 3 4 0
 -------
```

17
```
   4 3 5
 - 2 8 4
 -------
```

18
```
   8 6 1
 - 1 7 6
 -------
```

Write the missing number in the box.

1 $5 \times 4 =$ ☐

2 $3 \times 4 =$ ☐

3 $11 \times 4 =$ ☐

4 $7 \times 4 =$ ☐

5 $1 \times 4 =$ ☐

6 $6 \times 4 =$ ☐

7 $8 \times 4 =$ ☐

8 $10 \times 4 =$ ☐

9 $4 \times 4 =$ ☐

10 $12 \times 4 =$ ☐

11 $2 \times 4 =$ ☐

12 $9 \times 4 =$ ☐

13 $40 \div 4 =$ ☐

14 $8 \div 4 =$ ☐

15 $32 \div 4 =$ ☐

16 $20 \div 4 =$ ☐

17 $16 \div 4 =$ ☐

18 $28 \div 4 =$ ☐

19 $4 \div 4 =$ ☐

20 $48 \div 4 =$ ☐

21 $36 \div 4 =$ ☐

22 $12 \div 4 =$ ☐

23 $44 \div 4 =$ ☐

24 $24 \div 4 =$ ☐

25 ☐ $\div 4 = 4$

26 ☐ $\div 4 = 9$

27 ☐ $\div 4 = 3$

28 ☐ $\div 4 = 11$

29 ☐ $\div 4 = 2$

30 ☐ $\div 4 = 10$

31 ☐ $\div 4 = 6$

32 ☐ $\div 4 = 8$

33 ☐ $\div 4 = 5$

34 ☐ $\div 4 = 1$

35 ☐ $\div 4 = 12$

36 ☐ $\div 4 = 7$

37 ☐ $\times 4 = 28$

38 ☐ $\times 4 = 4$

39 ☐ $\times 4 = 24$

40 ☐ $\times 4 = 48$

41 ☐ $\times 4 = 40$

42 ☐ $\times 4 = 12$

43 ☐ $\times 4 = 20$

44 ☐ $\times 4 = 36$

45 ☐ $\times 4 = 8$

46 ☐ $\times 4 = 32$

37 ☐ $\times 4 = 16$

48 ☐ $\times 4 = 44$

Examples $240 \div 3 = 10 \times 24 \div 3$ $45 \div 5 = 9$
                        $= 10 \times 8$ $450 \div 5 = 90$
                        $= 80$

Fill in the boxes.

1 $25 \div 5 = \boxed{}$

  $250 \div 5 = \boxed{}$

2 $14 \div 2 = \boxed{}$

  $140 \div 2 = \boxed{}$

3 $24 \div 4 = \boxed{}$

  $240 \div 4 = \boxed{}$

4 $9 \div 3 = \boxed{}$

  $90 \div 3 = \boxed{}$

5 $24 \div 2 = \boxed{}$

  $240 \div 2 = \boxed{}$

6 $40 \div 5 = \boxed{}$

  $400 \div 5 = \boxed{}$

7 $18 \div 3 = \boxed{}$

  $180 \div 3 = \boxed{}$

8 $36 \div 4 = \boxed{}$

  $360 \div 4 = \boxed{}$

9 $33 \div 3 = \boxed{}$

  $330 \div 3 = \boxed{}$

10 $16 \div 2 = \boxed{}$

  $160 \div 2 = \boxed{}$

11 $16 \div 4 = \boxed{}$

  $160 \div 4 = \boxed{}$

12 $30 \div 5 = \boxed{}$

  $300 \div 5 = \boxed{}$

Work out

13 $120 \div 2$ ....

14 $100 \div 5$ ....

15 $270 \div 3$ ....

16 $200 \div 4$ ....

17 $350 \div 5$ ....

18 $60 \div 3$ ....

19 $480 \div 4$ ....

20 $80 \div 2$ ....

21 $450 \div 5$ ....

22 $880 \div 8$ ....

23 $240 \div 3$ ....

24 $100 \div 2$ ....

25 120 cakes
4 in each box

  $\boxed{}$ boxes

26 £150 prize
3 people

  £ $\boxed{}$ each

27 160 people
8 at each table

  $\boxed{}$ tables

28 180 litres of water
2 baths

  $\boxed{}$ litres each

29 400 pins
5 boxes

  $\boxed{}$ pins in each

30 280kg of potatoes
4 sacks

  $\boxed{}$ kg each

For each of the times:

a) draw the hands on the clock face

b) write the time in figures, using am and pm.

1. 25 past 9, bedtime

2. 20 past 3, night

3. $\frac{1}{4}$ to 2, afternoon

4. 5 past 11, morning

5. $\frac{1}{2}$ past 7, breakfast

6. 10 to 12, night

7. quarter past 6, evening

8. 10 o'clock, morning

9. 12 minutes past 9, morning

10. 17 minutes to 6, afternoon

11. 23 minutes past 12, lunchtime

12. 2 minutes to 12, lunchtime

1   ......9 : 25 pm......

4   ....

7   ....

10   ....

2   ....

5   ....

8   ....

11   ....

3   ....

6   ....

9   ....

12   ....

Colour in one part of the shape.
Write the fraction shown.

Colour in two parts of the shape.
Write the fraction shown.

Colour in the fraction shown.

 $\frac{9}{10}$  $\frac{1}{3}$  $\frac{4}{5}$ 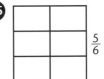 $\frac{5}{6}$

 $\frac{3}{4}$ 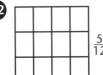 $\frac{5}{12}$ $\frac{7}{9}$ 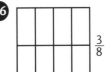 $\frac{3}{8}$

Write the fraction shown in each box.

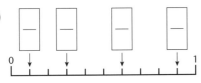

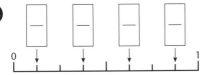

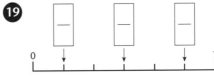

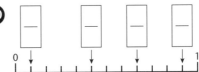

Use a set square to draw each shape.

1 a square   sides 3·3 cm

2 a rectangle   sides 2·9 cm, 5·3 cm

3 a square   perimeter 18 cm

4 a rectangle   perimeter 20 cm
longest side 6·5 cm

All lengths are in centimetres. Right angles are marked.
Measure and record the length of the longest side of each triangle.

5
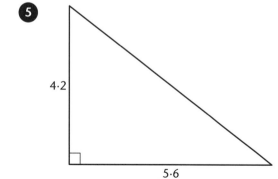

6
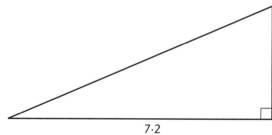

1 Use these words.   circle   pentagon   semi-circle
   Label the shapes.   hexagon   quadrilateral   square
                       octagon   rectangle

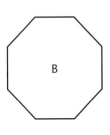

A

....

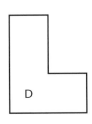

C

....

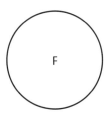

E

....

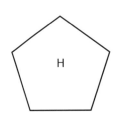

G

....

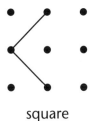

B

....

D

....

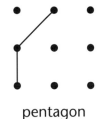

F

....

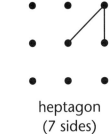

H

....

2 Write the letter of each shape which:

   a) is a polygon   ....

   b) is a non-polygon   ....

   c) is a quadrilateral   ....

   d) has all sides equal. ....

3 Draw a triangle with one angle larger than 90°.

4 Complete the shape in each grid. The shapes must have their corners on dots.

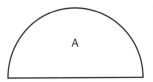

square

hexagon

pentagon

heptagon
(7 sides)

Examples	2 9	5 3
	× 3	× 4
	8 7	2 1 2
	2	1

Work out

1   3 7
    ×   2

2   6 5
    ×   3

3   2 9
    ×   4

4   7 4
    ×   5

5   5 9
    ×   2

6   4 8
    ×   3

7   8 4
    ×   4

8   3 7
    ×   5

9   8 2
    ×   2

10   7 3
    ×   3

11   6 5
    ×   4

12   9 2
    ×   5

13   5 6
    ×   3

14   7 8
    ×   4

15   6 4
    ×   2

Show your working. Write the answer in the box.

16 Cindy works 5 days.
She earns £86 each day.

She earns £ ☐ altogether.

17 There are 94 pins
in each packet.

There are ☐ pins in 3 packets.

× ‾‾‾‾‾‾‾

× ‾‾‾‾‾‾‾

Change to pence.

Change to pounds and pence.

1 £2·17   _217p_

5 £4·84   ....

9 351p   _£3·51_

13 129p   ....

2 £5·25   ....

6 £1·03   ....

10 8p   ....

14 465p   ....

3 £0·60   ....

7 £8·49   ....

11 913p   ....

15 702p   ....

4 £7·32   ....

8 £0·96   ....

12 670p   ....

16 94p   ....

17 £1 = [   ] × 10p

19 £2 = [   ] × 50p

21 £10 = [   ] × 50p

18 £1 = [   ] × 5p

20 £2 = [   ] × 20p

22 £10 = [   ] × 10p

23 Find the cost of these items and the change.

	Cost	Payment	Change
2 sweets at 37p each	74p	£1	....
10 drinks at 55p each	£5·50	£10	....
3 toys at £1·50 each	....	£5	....
4 books at £2·50 each	....	£10	....
2 pens at 99p each	....	£2	....
3 games at 80p each	....	£5	....

24 Use the above prices. Find the cost and the change.

	Cost	Payment	Change
a sweet, a drink	92p	£1	....
a pen, a book	....	£5	....
a toy, a game	....	£10	....
a book, a sweet	....	£5	....
a game, a pen	....	£2	....
a drink, a toy	....	£5	....

Write the missing numbers.

1 Ali cycles 79 miles on Saturday and 48 miles on Sunday.

He cycles ▢ miles altogether.

7 A ribbon is one metre long. 55 cm is cut off.

▢ cm is left.

2 Each packet of nuts weighs 60 g. The total weight of five packets is

▢ g.

8 Four identical lollies have a total weight of 360 g.

Each lolly weighs ▢ g.

3 A bottle of lemonade holds 1 litre. 500 ml is used.

▢ ml is left.

9 A small bottle of juice holds 450 ml. A large bottle holds 300 ml more.

A large bottle holds ▢ ml

4 The total length of three identical ropes is 210 m

Each rope is ▢ m long

10 One box is 60 cm wide
Two boxes have a total width of

▢ m ▢ cm

5 A baker uses 800 g of white flour and 500 g of brown flour

She uses ▢ g of flour altogether

11 A packet of cheese weighs 325 g 80 g is used

▢ g is left

6 A watering can holds 6 litres of water It is filled 8 times

▢ litres of water has been used

12 Two litres of drink is shared equally between 10 glasses

Each glass holds ▢ ml

Examples	$359 = 300 + 50 + 9$	$682 = 600 + 80 + 2$
	$= 350 + 9$	$= 680 + 2$
	$= 300 + 59$	$= 600 + 82$

Write the value of the underlined digit.

1 4<u>2</u>5 ....

2 16<u>9</u> ....

3 <u>5</u>03 ....

4 9<u>8</u>1 ....

5 <u>6</u>10 ....

6 37<u>4</u> ....

7 2<u>3</u>8 ....

8 <u>8</u>29 ....

9 7<u>5</u>6 ....

10 40<u>7</u> ....

11 <u>9</u>13 ....

12 12<u>6</u> ....

13 8<u>4</u>2 ....

14 <u>3</u>61 ....

15 5<u>7</u>9 ....

Write the missing number in the box.

16 $248 = 200 + 40 + \boxed{}$

17 $634 = 600 + \boxed{} + 4$

18 $187 = \boxed{} + 80 + 7$

19 $705 = 700 + \boxed{}$

20 $459 = \boxed{} + 50 + 9$

21 $963 = 900 + \boxed{} + 3$

22 $326 = 300 + 20 + \boxed{}$

23 $891 = \boxed{} + 90 + 1$

24 $272 = 200 + \boxed{} + 2$

25 $518 = \boxed{} + 10 + 8$

Write the missing number in the box.

26 $784 = 780 + \boxed{}$

27 $496 = 400 + \boxed{}$

28 $253 = \boxed{} + 3$

29 $675 = \boxed{} + 75$

30 $328 = 320 + \boxed{}$

31 $902 = 900 + \boxed{}$

32 $564 = 500 + \boxed{}$

33 $839 = \boxed{} + 9$

34 $147 = 140 + \boxed{}$

35 $393 = \boxed{} + 93$

Examples	Count on 4 from 259 $\longrightarrow$ 263
	Count on 50 from 259 $\longrightarrow$ 309
	Count on 300 from 259 $\longrightarrow$ 559

Count on

1 5 from 258   ....

2 4 from 786   ....

3 8 from 903   ....

4 6 from 349   ....

5 30 from 570   ....

6 70 from 852   ....

7 40 from 194   ....

8 50 from 761   ....

9 200 from 317   ....

10 500 from 285   ....

11 300 from 633   ....

12 400 from 429   ....

13 4 from 187   ....

14 7 from 708   ....

15 9 from 234   ....

16 5 from 419   ....

17 60 from 851   ....

18 80 from 396   ....

19 50 from 673   ....

20 70 from 962   ....

21 300 from 520   ....

22 500 from 435   ....

23 400 from 209   ....

24 600 from 157   ....

Complete by filling in the boxes.

25 454   455   456   457   ☐ ☐ ☐ ☐

26 835   845   855   865   ☐ ☐ ☐ ☐

27 197   297   397   497   ☐ ☐ ☐ ☐

28 586   587   588   589   ☐ ☐ ☐ ☐

29 763   773   783   793   ☐ ☐ ☐ ☐

30 18   118   218   318   ☐ ☐ ☐ ☐

Examples		2	8	5		4	3	7

Examples

```
    2 8 5          4 3 7
  + 2 4 9        + 1 6 7
    5 3 4          6 0 4
    1 1            1 1
```

Work out

1
```
    3 7 3
  + 3 4 5
  _____
```

2
```
    2 0 8
  + 1 9 3
  _____
```

3
```
    4 5 2
  + 2 6 7
  _____
```

4
```
    6 4 9
  + 1 2 8
  _____
```

5
```
    5 6 1
  + 2 8 6
  _____
```

6
```
    4 3 4
  + 1 7 5
  _____
```

7
```
    5 0 5
  + 3 7 9
  _____
```

8
```
    6 3 9
  + 3 4 5
  _____
```

9
```
    3 7 4
  + 2 9 7
  _____
```

10
```
    7 6 8
  + 1 5 4
  _____
```

11
```
    3 2 7
  + 2 8 5
  _____
```

12
```
    5 9 3
  + 1 3 8
  _____
```

13
```
    4 5 6
  + 3 5 7
  _____
```

14
```
    3 8 2
  + 1 6 4
  _____
```

15
```
    6 0 9
  + 2 8 6
  _____
```

16
```
    5 4 4
  + 3 6 9
  _____
```

17
```
    4 9 8
  + 4 4 2
  _____
```

18
```
    6 7 5
  + 1 6 8
  _____
```

Examples	^{7} ^{10} ^{1}	^{5} ^{13} ^{1}
	8̶ 1̶0̶ 7	6̶ 4̶ 5
	− 6 5 8	− 2 4 9
	1 5 9	3 9 6

Work out

1
```
    3 7 3
−   1 4 5
_____
```

2
```
    7 5 6
−   3 8 0
_____
```

3
```
    5 9 0
−   2 7 4
_____
```

4
```
    2 2 5
−   1 6 3
_____
```

5
```
    9 8 4
−   5 2 7
_____
```

6
```
    4 1 4
−   2 3 0
_____
```

7
```
    8 4 8
−   4 9 5
_____
```

8
```
    6 6 1
−   3 5 4
_____
```

9
```
    3 3 7
−   2 9 2
_____
```

10
```
    5 8 5
−   3 1 7
_____
```

11
```
    4 6 9
−   1 7 4
_____
```

12
```
    9 5 2
−   2 5 8
_____
```

13
```
    7 9 4
−   2 9 6
_____
```

14
```
    5 2 8
−   1 3 8
_____
```

15
```
    8 4 6
−   5 8 2
_____
```

16
```
    4 1 5
−   3 6 6
_____
```

17
```
    9 7 0
−   3 8 5
_____
```

18
```
    6 5 3
−   4 9 7
_____
```

Examples	$7 \times 3 = 21$	$5 \times 8 = 40$
	$70 \times 3 = 210$	$50 \times 8 = 400$

Work out

1 5×50 ....

2 4×80 ....

3 60×4 ....

4 50×2 ....

5 3×30 ....

6 8×50 ....

7 20×2 ....

8 90×8 ....

9 3×40 ....

10 11×50 ....

11 90×3 ....

12 80×2 ....

13 4×20 ....

14 6×80 ....

15 90×4 ....

16 110×3 ....

17 2×50 ....

18 8×80 ....

19 90×2 ....

20 50×4 ....

21 6×30 ....

22 3×50 ....

23 70×4 ....

24 120×8 ....

25 12×30 ....

26 11×20 ....

27 50×5 ....

28 70×8 ....

29 4×40 ....

30 8×30 ....

31 60×5 ....

32 70×2 ....

33 9×80 ....

34 2×30 ....

35 120×4 ....

36 70×5 ....

Fill in the boxes.

37 One minute is 60 seconds.

8 minutes is ☐ seconds.

38 Each bucket holds 5 litres.

30 buckets hold ☐ litres.

39 Laura has nine £20 notes.

She has £ ☐ .

40 Each box has 12 eggs.

40 boxes hold ☐ eggs.

41 One ice cream costs 90p.

3 ice creams cost £ ☐

42 Seven days in one week.

☐ days in 20 weeks.

> *Examples* $240 \div 3 = 10 \times 24 \div 3$ $45 \div 5 = 9$
> $= 10 \times 8$ $450 \div 5 = 90$
> $= 80$

Work out

1   $80 \div 4$ ....
2   $120 \div 2$ ....
3   $560 \div 8$ ....
4   $150 \div 3$ ....

5   $160 \div 8$ ....
6   $400 \div 5$ ....
7   $80 \div 2$ ....
8   $360 \div 4$ ....

9   $210 \div 3$ ....
10   $960 \div 8$ ....
11   $200 \div 5$ ....
12   $220 \div 2$ ....

13   $90 \div 3$ ....
14   $440 \div 4$ ....
15   $640 \div 8$ ....
16   $350 \div 5$ ....

17   $40 \div 2$ ....
18   $320 \div 4$ ....
19   $360 \div 3$ ....
20   $240 \div 8$ ....

21   $600 \div 5$ ....
22   $120 \div 4$ ....
23   $140 \div 2$ ....
24   $270 \div 3$ ....

25   $300 \div 5$ ....
26   $880 \div 8$ ....
27   $240 \div 3$ ....
28   $100 \div 2$ ....

29   $480 \div 4$ ....
30   $720 \div 8$ ....
31   $250 \div 5$ ....
32   $180 \div 3$ ....

33   $240 \div 2$ ....
34   $480 \div 8$ ....
35   $450 \div 5$ ....
36   $280 \div 4$ ....

Fill in the boxes.

37   240 rolls
4 in each box

[   ] boxes

38   400 g cake
8 slices

Each slice is [   ] g.

39   120 children in
3 coaches

[   ] children
in each coach.

40   £5 notes only
£550 altogether

[   ] notes

41   60 g cornflakes
2 bowls

[   ] g in each bowl

42   4 chairs cost
£160 altogether. Each

chair costs £ [   ] .

Examples

40 mm = 4 cm	1000 g = 1 kg	1000 ml = 1 litre (ℓ)
130 cm = 1 m 30 cm	3200 g = 3 kg 200 g	4700 ml = 4 ℓ 700 ml
2500 m = 2 km 500 m	600 g = 0 kg 600 g	8500 ml = 8 ℓ 500 ml

Count on

1 500 cm = ☐ m

2 2000 g = ☐ kg

3 100 mm = ☐ cm

4 4000 ml = ☐ litres

5 1 km = ☐ m

6 5 kg = ☐ g

7 8 m = ☐ cm

8 2 litres = ☐ ml

9 60 mm = ☐ cm

10 1000 ml = ☐ litre

11 4000 m = ☐ km

12 9000 g = ☐ kg

13 2 m = ☐ cm

14 7 litres = ☐ ml

15 5 cm = ☐ mm

16 3 kg = ☐ g

17 3 ℓ 500 ml = ☐ ml

18 0 km 300 m = ☐ m

19 4 kg 600 g = ☐ g

20 1 m 90 cm = ☐ cm

21 6900 ml = ☐ ℓ ☐ ml

22 37 mm = ☐ cm ☐ mm

23 1200 g = ☐ kg ☐ g

24 5400 m = ☐ km ☐ m

25 7 m 90 cm = ☐ cm

26 0 kg 700 g = ☐ g

27 8 cm 2 mm = ☐ mm

28 1 ℓ 300 ml = ☐ ml

29 2800 m = ☐ km ☐ m

30 8500 g = ☐ kg ☐ g

31 450 cm = ☐ m ☐ cm

32 100 ml = ☐ ℓ ☐ ml

1 This table shows the number of soft toys sold in a toy shop.

Soft toys	Number sold
Bears	80
Cats	50
Dolls	90
Monkeys	40
Pigs	70

Complete the bar chart to show the data in the table.

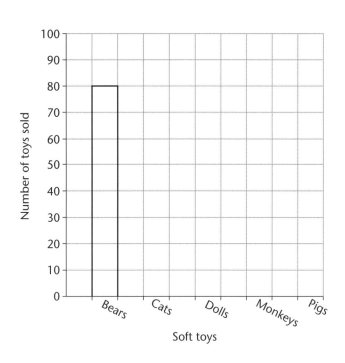

2 Each child in Year 3 was asked to choose their favourite percussion instrument. These are the results.

Instruments	Votes
Bongos	20
Drum	12
Maracas	24
Shaker	10
Tambourine	18

Complete the bar chart to show the results. Label the bar chart in 2s.

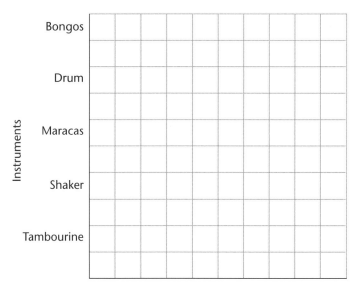

Number of votes

Examples	6 + 7 = 13	12 − 4 = 8
	60 + 70 = 130	120 − 40 = 80

Work out

1 30 + 80   ....

2 120 + 60   ....

3 70 + 40   ....

4 80 + 50   ....

5 50 + 70   ....

6 90 + 60   ....

7 140 + 50   ....

8 40 + 90   ....

9 60 + 60   ....

10 80 + 90   ....

11 130 + 70   ....

12 90 + 90   ....

13 20 + 80   ....

14 70 + 80   ....

15 120 + 40   ....

16 60 + 80   ....

17 90 + 30   ....

18 50 + 90   ....

19 80 + 40   ....

20 110 + 70   ....

21 140 − 80   ....

22 150 − 60   ....

23 160 − 110   ....

24 120 − 70   ....

25 110 − 40   ....

26 200 − 140   ....

27 130 − 50   ....

28 160 − 90   ....

29 120 − 30   ....

30 140 − 70   ....

31 160 − 80   ....

32 130 − 60   ....

33 170 − 90   ....

34 120 − 40   ....

35 200 − 110   ....

36 110 − 60   ....

37 190 − 120   ....

38 160 − 70   ....

39 130 − 90   ....

40 180 − 130   ....

Example

5 + 9 = 14
17 − 9 = 8
14 + 17 = 31

```
        31
    14     17
  5    9    8
```

Fill in the boxes to complete the addition pyramids.

1
```
     □
   □   □
  6  4  7
```

6
```
        27
     16    □
   11   □   □
```

2
```
     □
   □   □
  8  4  8
```

7
```
        38
     □     □
   □    4    7
```

3
```
     □
  12   17
 □  □    9
```

8
```
    □
  11   15
 2   □   □
```

4
```
     □
   □   20
  4  □   11
```

9
```
        40
     □     20
   □    8    □
```

5
```
     □
   □   14
  7  11   □
```

10
```
        35
     □     16
   □    □    9
```

Write the missing number in the box.

1 4 × 8 = ☐

2 10 × 8 = ☐

3 1 × 8 = ☐

4 8 × 8 = ☐

5 11 × 8 = ☐

6 2 × 8 = ☐

7 9 × 8 = ☐

8 6 × 8 = ☐

9 3 × 8 = ☐

10 5 × 8 = ☐

11 12 × 8 = ☐

12 7 × 8 = ☐

13 48 ÷ 8 = ☐

14 88 ÷ 8 = ☐

15 24 ÷ 8 = ☐

16 72 ÷ 8 = ☐

17 8 ÷ 8 = ☐

18 56 ÷ 8 = ☐

19 40 ÷ 8 = ☐

20 96 ÷ 8 = ☐

21 32 ÷ 8 = ☐

22 80 ÷ 8 = ☐

23 16 ÷ 8 = ☐

24 64 ÷ 8 = ☐

25 ☐ × 8 = 40

26 ☐ × 8 = 8

27 ☐ × 8 = 80

28 ☐ × 8 = 64

29 ☐ × 8 = 16

30 ☐ × 8 = 56

31 ☐ × 8 = 32

32 ☐ × 8 = 88

33 ☐ × 8 = 72

34 ☐ × 8 = 48

35 ☐ × 8 = 24

36 ☐ × 8 = 96

37 ☐ ÷ 8 = 7

38 ☐ ÷ 8 = 11

39 ☐ ÷ 8 = 6

40 ☐ ÷ 8 = 2

41 ☐ ÷ 8 = 12

42 ☐ ÷ 8 = 3

43 ☐ ÷ 8 = 5

44 ☐ ÷ 8 = 8

45 ☐ ÷ 8 = 10

46 ☐ ÷ 8 = 1

37 ☐ ÷ 8 = 9

48 ☐ ÷ 8 = 4

Examples

$$\begin{array}{r} 7\ 3 \\ \times\ \underline{\quad 5} \\ 3\ 6\ 5 \\ \hline {\scriptstyle 1} \end{array} \qquad \begin{array}{r} 2\ 6 \\ \times\ \underline{\quad 8} \\ 2\ 0\ 8 \\ \hline {\scriptstyle 4} \end{array}$$

Work out

1
$$\begin{array}{r} 3\ 4 \\ \times\ \underline{\quad 4} \end{array}$$

2
$$\begin{array}{r} 7\ 5 \\ \times\ \underline{\quad 2} \end{array}$$

3
$$\begin{array}{r} 6\ 7 \\ \times\ \underline{\quad 3} \end{array}$$

4
$$\begin{array}{r} 9\ 8 \\ \times\ \underline{\quad 5} \end{array}$$

5
$$\begin{array}{r} 6\ 4 \\ \times\ \underline{\quad 8} \end{array}$$

6
$$\begin{array}{r} 8\ 6 \\ \times\ \underline{\quad 4} \end{array}$$

7
$$\begin{array}{r} 4\ 8 \\ \times\ \underline{\quad 2} \end{array}$$

8
$$\begin{array}{r} 5\ 4 \\ \times\ \underline{\quad 3} \end{array}$$

9
$$\begin{array}{r} 7\ 8 \\ \times\ \underline{\quad 8} \end{array}$$

10
$$\begin{array}{r} 6\ 5 \\ \times\ \underline{\quad 5} \end{array}$$

11
$$\begin{array}{r} 9\ 7 \\ \times\ \underline{\quad 4} \end{array}$$

12
$$\begin{array}{r} 3\ 9 \\ \times\ \underline{\quad 3} \end{array}$$

13
$$\begin{array}{r} 5\ 9 \\ \times\ \underline{\quad 8} \end{array}$$

14
$$\begin{array}{r} 4\ 7 \\ \times\ \underline{\quad 5} \end{array}$$

15
$$\begin{array}{r} 8\ 6 \\ \times\ \underline{\quad 3} \end{array}$$

Show your working. Write the answer in the box.

16 Each cake weighs 93 g.
8 cakes weigh

☐ g altogether.

$$\times\ \underline{\qquad}$$

17 There are 75 children in
each Year of a school.

☐ children in all 4 years.

$$\times\ \underline{\qquad}$$

Examples	$\dfrac{1\ 4}{5\overline{)7^20}}$		$\dfrac{2\ 6}{3\overline{)7^18}}$

Work out

1 $2\overline{)6\ 8}$

2 $3\overline{)3\ 9}$

3 $4\overline{)8\ 0}$

4 $2\overline{)4\ 6}$

5 $5\overline{)9\ 5}$

6 $3\overline{)7\ 2}$

7 $4\overline{)6\ 0}$

8 $2\overline{)5\ 2}$

9 $3\overline{)9\ 6}$

10 $5\overline{)8\ 0}$

11 $2\overline{)3\ 8}$

12 $4\overline{)9\ 2}$

13 $5\overline{)6\ 5}$

14 $3\overline{)5\ 1}$

15 $2\overline{)9\ 0}$

16 $4\overline{)7\ 2}$

17 $3\overline{)8\ 4}$

18 $2\overline{)7\ 4}$

Show your working. Write the answer in the box

19 Four pencils cost 76p altogether.

One pencil costs ☐ p.

20 3 equal size classes in Year 4

81 children ☐ in each class.

Read the measurements shown on each ruler to the nearest millimetre.

1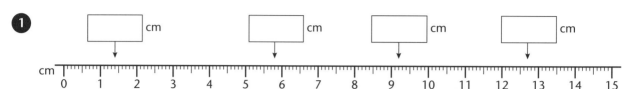

2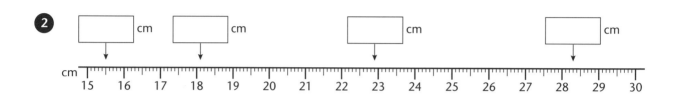

Measure these lines to the nearest millimetre.

3 _____ [ ] cm

4 _____ [ ] cm

5 _____ [ ] cm

6 _____ [ ] cm

7 _____ [ ] cm

Draw lines of the following lengths.

8 8.5 cm ....

9 11.1 cm ....

10 4.7 cm ....

11 7.3 cm ....

12 9.6 cm ....

Examples

$\frac{1}{4}$ of 20 = 20 ÷ 4

= 5

$\frac{3}{4}$ of 20 = (20 ÷ 4) × 3

= 15

Find $\frac{1}{2}$ of:

1 14 ....

2 8 ....

3 18 ....

4 24 ....

Find $\frac{1}{3}$ of:

5 18 ....

6 33 ....

7 24 ....

8 30 ....

Find $\frac{1}{10}$ of:

9 90 ....

10 30 ....

11 50 ....

12 100 ....

Find

13 $\frac{1}{2}$ of 12 ....

14 $\frac{1}{4}$ of 28 ....

15 $\frac{1}{5}$ of 45 ....

16 $\frac{1}{10}$ of 120 ....

17 $\frac{1}{3}$ of 27 ....

18 $\frac{1}{8}$ of 40 ....

19 $\frac{1}{2}$ of 22 ....

20 $\frac{1}{4}$ of 36 ....

21 $\frac{1}{5}$ of 30 ....

22 $\frac{1}{10}$ of 80 ....

23 $\frac{1}{3}$ of 36 ....

24 $\frac{1}{8}$ of 64 ....

Look at the circles. Find

25 $\frac{1}{3}$ of 15 ....

26 $\frac{2}{3}$ of 15 ....

27 $\frac{1}{5}$ of 15 ....

28 $\frac{2}{5}$ of 15 ....

29 $\frac{4}{5}$ of 15 ....

How much is:

30 one tenth of £60 ....

31 one half of £60 ....

32 one fifth of £60? ....

33 one half of 800 g ....

34 one quarter of 800 g ....

35 one eighth of 800 g? ....

Shade in each pair of fractions to show that they are equivalent fractions.
Fill in the boxes.

1 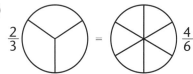 $\frac{2}{3}$ = $\frac{4}{6}$

5 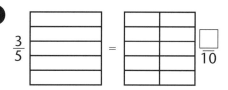 $\frac{3}{5}$ = $\frac{\square}{10}$

2 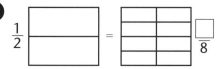 $\frac{1}{2}$ = $\frac{\square}{8}$

6 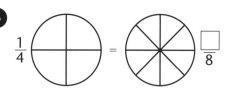 $\frac{1}{4}$ = $\frac{\square}{8}$

3 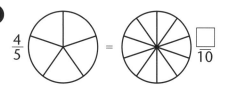 $\frac{4}{5}$ = $\frac{\square}{10}$

7 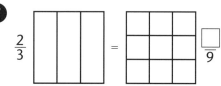 $\frac{2}{3}$ = $\frac{\square}{9}$

4 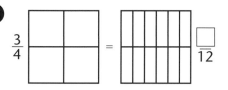 $\frac{3}{4}$ = $\frac{\square}{12}$

8 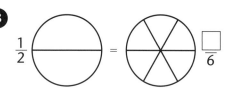 $\frac{1}{2}$ = $\frac{\square}{6}$

Use the fraction charts to complete these equivalent fractions.

whole	
half	
quarter	
eighth	

whole	
third	
sixth	
twelfth	

9 $\frac{1}{2}$ = $\frac{\square}{4}$ **11** $\frac{3}{4}$ = $\frac{\square}{8}$ **13** $\frac{1}{4}$ = $\frac{\square}{8}$ **15** 1 = $\frac{\square}{8}$

10 $\frac{1}{6}$ = $\frac{\square}{12}$ **12** $\frac{2}{3}$ = $\frac{\square}{6}$ **14** $\frac{5}{6}$ = $\frac{\square}{12}$ **16** $\frac{1}{3}$ = $\frac{\square}{12}$

Write down the time if the hour hand turns these angles from:

| 12 o'clock |

| 4 o'clock |

1 a half turn   *6 o'clock* ....

2 a right angle   ....

3 a whole turn   ....

4 a $\frac{3}{4}$ turn   ....

5 a whole turn   ....

6 a right angle   ....

7 a $\frac{3}{4}$ turn   ....

8 a half turn   ....

Are these compass movements right angles, half turns or three quarter turns.

| Turn clockwise |

| Turn anti-clockwise |

9 N to S   *half turn* ....

10 E to N   ....

11 S to W   ....

12 W to E   ....

13 E to S   ....

14 S to E   ....

15 N to E   ....

16 W to S   ....

Decide if each angle is a right angle or smaller than or larger than a right angle.
Write right angle, smaller or larger on each line.

17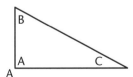

18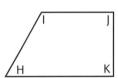

19

A   ....

B   ....

C   ....

D   ....

E   ....

F   ....

G   ....

H   ....

I   ....

J   ....

K   ....

1 Delon has 14 socks.

How many pairs does he have?

2 Sixty chairs are set out in five equal rows.

How many chairs are there in each row?

3 A group of children have 36 straws.

How many triangles can they make?

4 A class of 32 children sit at tables of four.

How many tables are there?

5 A test has 20 questions. Marnie gets one tenth wrong.

How many does she get wrong?

6 There are 240 children in a school. They are in eight equal classes.

How many children are there in each class?

7 Fern is driving 180 miles. She is half way.

How far has she driven?   miles

8 Thirty cherries are shared equally between six children.

How many do they have each?

9 A packet of three T-shirts costs £18.

What does one T-shirt cost?

10 A book has 160 pages. Nick has read one quarter of the book.

How many pages has he read?

11 Zoe saves 10p coins. She has saved £2.50.

How many coins has she saved?

12 Forty balls fit exactly into eight equal size bags.

How many balls are there in each bag?

Work out

1   356 m + 5 m   ....m

2   817 g + 7 g   ....g

3   £468 + £9   £..................

4   237 km + 4 km   ....km

5   783 ml + 8 ml   ....ml

6   £948 + £6   £..................

7   238 m + 90 m   ....m

8   542 kg + 60 kg   ....kg

9   £195 + £30   £..................

10   783 km + 50 km   ....km

11   696 ml + 70 ml   ....ml

12   £361 + £80   £..................

13   524 m + 400 m   ....m

14   57 g + 800 g   ....g

15   £579 + £200   £..................

16   142 km + 400 km   ....km

17   410 ml + 200 ml   ....ml

18   £688 + £300   £..................

19   £274 − £6   £..................

20   153 km − 9 km   ....km

21   936 kg − 8 kg   ....kg

22   £342 − £7   £..................

23   781 m − 5 m   ....m

24   423 ml − 4 ml   ....ml

25   £569 − £70   £..................

26   827 km − 50 km   ....km

27   615 g − 60 g   ....g

28   £424 − £80   £..................

29   208 m − 40 m   ....m

30   772 ml − 90 ml   ....ml

31   £941 − £400   £..................

32   536 km − 300 km   ....km

33   803 kg − 200 kg   ....kg

34   £795 − £300   £..................

35   649 m − 400 m   ....m

36   964 ml − 800 ml   ....ml

For each of the times:

a) draw the hands on the clock face

b) write the time in figures, using am and pm.

1. 10 to 8, breakfast

2. quarter past 3, hometime

3. 25 past 11, night

4. 20 to 6, sunrise

5. 3 minutes to 7, evening

6. 8 minutes past 10, morning

7. quarter to 9, bedtime

8. 22 minutes past 12, lunchtime

9. 24 minutes to 3, night

10. 14 minutes past 7, morning

11. 1 minute to 11, night

12. 3 minutes past 4, afternoon

7 : 50 am

Examples	$592 = 500 + 90 + 2$	$675 = 600 + 70 + 5$
	$= 590 + 2$	$= 670 + 5$
	$= 500 + 92$	$= 600 + 75$
	$= 502 + 90$	$= 605 + 70$

Partition these numbers.

1 $376 = \boxed{} + \boxed{} + \boxed{}$

2 $848 = \boxed{} + \boxed{} + \boxed{}$

3 $583 = \boxed{} + \boxed{} + \boxed{}$

4 $961 = \boxed{} + \boxed{} + \boxed{}$

5 $415 = \boxed{} + \boxed{} + \boxed{}$

6 $632 = \boxed{} + \boxed{} + \boxed{}$

7 $257 = \boxed{} + \boxed{} + \boxed{}$

8 $729 = \boxed{} + \boxed{} + \boxed{}$

9 $134 = \boxed{} + \boxed{} + \boxed{}$

10 $569 = \boxed{} + \boxed{} + \boxed{}$

11 $296 = \boxed{} + \boxed{} + \boxed{}$

12 $718 = \boxed{} + \boxed{} + \boxed{}$

Write the missing number in the box.

13 $437 = 430 + \boxed{}$

14 $181 = 100 + \boxed{}$

15 $792 = \boxed{} + 92$

16 $265 = \boxed{} + 5$

17 $943 = 903 + \boxed{}$

18 $526 = \boxed{} + 20$

19 $459 = 450 + \boxed{}$

20 $874 = 800 + \boxed{}$

21 $351 = \boxed{} + 51$

22 $614 = 604 + \boxed{}$

23 $128 = \boxed{} + 8$

24 $579 = \boxed{} + 70$

25 $762 = 760 + \boxed{}$

26 $495 = 400 + \boxed{}$

27 $247 = \boxed{} + 7$

28 $986 = 906 + \boxed{}$

> **Example**   Start at 0. Count on 4 steps of 50.
>
> 0   50   100   150   200   Answer *200*

Count on

1 5 steps of 4 ....

2 4 steps of 8 ....

3 3 steps of 50 ....

4 5 steps of 100 ....

5 8 steps of 4 ....

6 7 steps of 8 ....

7 6 steps of 50 ....

8 9 steps of 100 ....

9 6 steps of 4 ....

10 10 steps of 8 ....

11 7 steps of 50 ....

12 4 steps of 100 ....

13 7 steps of 4 ....

14 5 steps of 8 ....

15 4 steps of 50 ....

16 8 steps of 100 ....

17 12 steps of 4 ....

18 9 steps of 8 ....

19 5 steps of 50 ....

20 6 steps of 100 ....

21 9 steps of 4 ....

22 6 steps of 8 ....

23 8 steps of 50 ....

24 10 steps of 100? ....

Complete by filling in the boxes.

25   4   8   ☐   16   ☐   ☐   28   ☐   36   ☐

26   ☐   16   ☐   32   ☐   48   56   ☐   72   ☐

27   50   100   ☐   200   250   ☐   ☐   400   ☐   ☐

28   100   200   ☐   ☐   500   600   ☐   800   ☐   ☐

29   53   153   253   ☐   453   ☐   ☐   753   ☐   ☐

30   6   56   106   156   ☐   ☐   ☐   ☐   456

Examples	$100 - 57 = \boxed{}$	$112 - 57 = \boxed{}$
	$57 \longrightarrow 60 = 3$	$57 \longrightarrow 100 = 43$
	$60 \longrightarrow 100 = 40$	$100 \longrightarrow 112 = 12$
	Answer *43*	Answer *55*

Work out

1 $100 - 40 = \boxed{}$

2 $100 - 70 = \boxed{}$

3 $100 - 5 = \boxed{}$

4 $100 - 55 = \boxed{}$

5 $100 - 38 = \boxed{}$

6 $100 - 91 = \boxed{}$

7 $100 - 19 = \boxed{}$

8 $100 - 74 = \boxed{}$

9 $\boxed{} + 10 = 100$

10 $\boxed{} + 60 = 100$

11 $\boxed{} + 25 = 100$

12 $\boxed{} + 85 = 100$

13 $\boxed{} + 46 = 100$

14 $\boxed{} + 63 = 100$

15 $\boxed{} + 7 = 100$

16 $\boxed{} + 82 = 100$

17 $110 - 33$ ....

18 $130 - 64$ ....

19 $105 - 76$ ....

20 $143 - 85$ ....

21 $125 - 79$ ....

22 $137 - 92$ ....

23 $104 - 47$ ....

24 $119 - 35$ ....

25 $156 - 88$ ....

26 $122 - 96$ ....

27 $113 - 59$ ....

28 $141 - 62$ ....

29 $108 - 24$ ....

30 $136 - 89$ ....

31 $114 - 75$ ....

32 $123 - 58$ ....

Fill in the boxes.

1 $36 + 27 = 36 + 20 + \boxed{}$

$ = 56 + \boxed{}$

$ = \boxed{}$

2 $59 + 32 = 59 + \boxed{} + 2$

$ = \boxed{} + 2$

$ = \boxed{}$

3 $65 + 59 = 65 + \boxed{} + \boxed{}$

$ = \boxed{} + \boxed{}$

$ = \boxed{}$

4 $97 + 45 = \boxed{} + \boxed{} + \boxed{}$

$ = \boxed{} + \boxed{}$

$ = \boxed{}$

5 $82 - 55 = 82 - 50 - \boxed{}$

$ = 32 - \boxed{}$

$ = \boxed{}$

6 $95 - 26 = 95 - \boxed{} - 6$

$ = \boxed{} - 6$

$ = \boxed{}$

7 $127 - 49 = 127 - \boxed{} - \boxed{}$

$ = \boxed{} - \boxed{}$

$ = \boxed{}$

8 $103 - 37 = \boxed{} - \boxed{} - \boxed{}$

$ = \boxed{} - \boxed{}$

$ = \boxed{}$

Work out by partitioning.

9 $46 + 35$ ....

10 $78 + 28$ ....

11 $38 + 34$ ....

12 $89 + 56$ ....

13 $67 + 47$ ....

14 $54 + 29$ ....

15 $96 + 68$ ....

16 $79 + 47$ ....

17 $64 - 37$ ....

18 $91 - 46$ ....

19 $72 - 58$ ....

20 $115 - 29$ ....

21 $143 - 75$ ....

22 $86 - 37$ ....

23 $124 - 89$ ....

24 $131 - 43$ ....

Write the missing number in the box.

1 $2 \times 2 =$ ☐

2 $8 \times 2 =$ ☐

3 $11 \times 2 =$ ☐

4 ☐ $\times 2 = 12$

5 ☐ $\times 2 = 10$

6 ☐ $\times 2 = 18$

7 ☐ $\div 2 = 4$

8 ☐ $\div 2 = 12$

9 ☐ $\div 2 = 7$

10 $6 \times 5 =$ ☐

11 $3 \times 5 =$ ☐

12 $12 \times 5 =$ ☐

13 ☐ $\times 5 = 5$

14 ☐ $\times 5 = 45$

15 ☐ $\times 5 = 35$

16 ☐ $\div 5 = 11$

17 ☐ $\div 5 = 10$

18 ☐ $\div 5 = 8$

19 $10 \times 10 =$ ☐

20 $7 \times 10 =$ ☐

21 $9 \times 10 =$ ☐

22 ☐ $\times 10 = 40$

23 ☐ $\times 10 = 120$

24 ☐ $\times 10 = 80$

25 ☐ $\div 10 = 2$

26 ☐ $\div 10 = 6$

27 ☐ $\div 10 = 11$

28 $5 \times 3 =$ ☐

29 $11 \times 3 =$ ☐

30 $8 \times 3 =$ ☐

31 ☐ $\times 3 = 18$

32 ☐ $\times 3 = 9$

33 ☐ $\times 3 = 27$

34 ☐ $\div 3 = 1$

35 ☐ $\div 3 = 12$

36 ☐ $\div 3 = 7$

37 $6 \times 4 =$ ☐

38 $1 \times 4 =$ ☐

39 $12 \times 4 =$ ☐

40 ☐ $\times 4 = 8$

41 ☐ $\times 4 = 44$

42 ☐ $\times 4 = 28$

43 ☐ $\div 4 = 5$

44 ☐ $\div 4 = 8$

45 ☐ $\div 4 = 9$

46 $4 \times 8 =$ ☐

47 $9 \times 8 =$ ☐

48 $7 \times 8 =$ ☐

49 ☐ $\times 8 = 80$

50 ☐ $\times 8 = 64$

51 ☐ $\times 8 = 96$

52 ☐ $\div 8 = 3$

53 ☐ $\div 8 = 11$

54 ☐ $\div 8 = 6$

Examples	$\begin{array}{r} 2\ 3 \\ 4\overline{)9\ ^1 2} \end{array}$	$\begin{array}{r} 1\ 5 \\ 8\overline{)1\ 2\ ^4 0} \end{array}$

Work out

1 $2\overline{)8\ 6}$

2 $3\overline{)4\ 8}$

3 $5\overline{)7\ 0}$

4 $4\overline{)5\ 2}$

5 $8\overline{)9\ 6}$

6 $2\overline{)3\ 6}$

7 $3\overline{)7\ 5}$

8 $4\overline{)9\ 6}$

9 $2\overline{)5\ 8}$

10 $5\overline{)8\ 5}$

11 $3\overline{)5\ 4}$

12 $4\overline{)7\ 6}$

13 $8\overline{)1\ 1\ 2}$

14 $2\overline{)7\ 0}$

15 $3\overline{)8\ 7}$

16 $4\overline{)6\ 8}$

17 $5\overline{)1\ 0\ 0}$

18 $2\overline{)9\ 4}$

Show your working. Write the answer in the box.

19 4 people at each table.

72 people [   ] tables.

20 78 children.

Half are boys [   ] boys.

Write each measurement in the box.

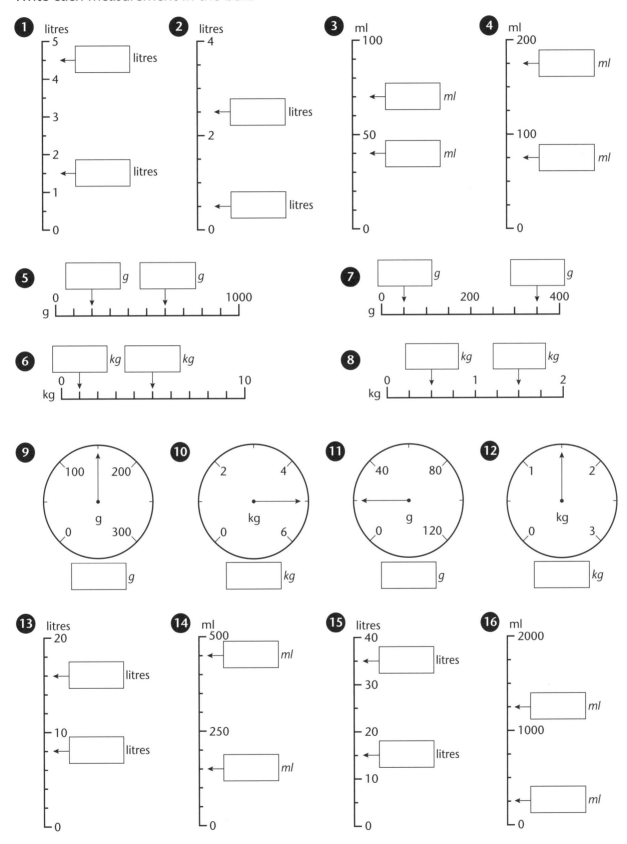

Write the missing numbers.

1 Grandad weighs 84 kg.
Grandma weighs 29 kg less.

Grandma weighs ☐ kg.

7 A bag of potatoes weighs 2 kg.
700 g is used.

☐ kg ☐ g is left.

2 A swimming pool is 12 m wide.
It is three times as long.

The pool is ☐ m long.

8 A tape is one metre long.
It is cut into 5 equal lengths.

Each length is ☐ cm long.

3 A bottle of medicine holds 100 ml.
Four 20 ml doses are taken.

☐ ml is left.

9 Dad's bath uses 68 litres of water.
Mum's shower uses 35 litres.

☐ litres of water is used altogether.

4 A cake weighs 320 g.
It is cut into 8 equal slices.

Each slice weighs ☐ g.

10 Each bag of cement weighs 30 kg.
The total weight of four bags is

☐ kg.

5 A field is 70 m longer than it is wide.
It is 273 m wide.

It is ☐ m long.

11 Lisa's journey is 162 miles long.
She drives 97 miles.

She has ☐ miles left to drive.

6 A tube of toothpaste holds 75 ml.

Ten tubes hold ☐ ml altogether.

12 A large bottle of drink holds 700ml.
A small bottle holds half as much.

A small bottle holds ☐ ml.

This bar chart shows the colour of the carpets sold in a showroom.

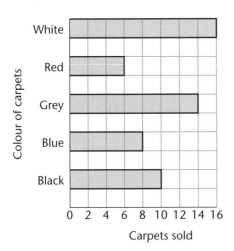

This bar chart shows the ages of children in a junior choir.

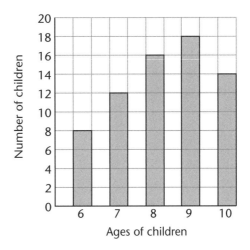

1 How many people bought:

a) a blue carpet   ....

b) a white carpet?   ....

2 Which colour carpet was bought by:

a) 14 people   ....

b) 10 people?   ....

3 How many more black carpets were sold than blue carpets?

....

4 How many fewer red carpets were sold than white carpets?

....

5 How many carpets were sold altogether?

....

6 How many carpets sold were either grey or white?   ....

7 How many 8 year old children are in the choir?   ....

8 How many more 9 year old children are in the choir than 10 year old children?   ....

9 How many fewer children are there aged 6 than 7?   ....

10 How many children are there:

a) younger than 8   ....

b) older than 8?   ....

11 How many children are there in the choir altogether?   ....

12 Half the choir are either

⬜ or ⬜ years old.

Examples $85 + \boxed{} = 109$ $\boxed{} - 50 = 279$
$109 - 85 = 24$ $279 + 50 = 329$
Missing number is 24   Missing number is 329

Write the missing number in the box.

1 $65 + \boxed{} = 100$

2 $12 + \boxed{} = 100$

3 $47 + \boxed{} = 100$

4 $100 - \boxed{} = 29$

5 $100 - \boxed{} = 84$

6 $100 - \boxed{} = 56$

7 $\boxed{} + 6 = 125$

8 $\boxed{} + 9 = 793$

9 $\boxed{} + 5 = 342$

10 $\boxed{} - 8 = 867$

11 $\boxed{} - 4 = 438$

12 $\boxed{} - 7 = 250$

13 $48 + \boxed{} = 71$

14 $65 + \boxed{} = 110$

15 $87 + \boxed{} = 146$

16 $93 - \boxed{} = 65$

17 $121 - \boxed{} = 79$

18 $104 - \boxed{} = 47$

19 $\boxed{} + 50 = 478$

20 $\boxed{} + 20 = 305$

21 $\boxed{} + 60 = 823$

22 $\boxed{} - 30 = 539$

23 $\boxed{} - 70 = 266$

24 $\boxed{} - 40 = 772$

25 $59 + \boxed{} = 95$

26 $96 + \boxed{} = 161$

27 $74 + \boxed{} = 122$

28 $81 - \boxed{} = 37$

29 $115 - \boxed{} = 86$

30 $132 - \boxed{} = 59$

31 $\boxed{} + 300 = 946$

32 $\boxed{} + 500 = 782$

33 $\boxed{} + 200 = 617$

34 $\boxed{} - 400 = 190$

35 $\boxed{} - 300 = 453$

36 $\boxed{} - 600 = 238$

Write the answer in the box.

1 59 boys
55 girls

[   ] children

2 217 apples on a tree.
60 picked.

[   ] left

3 Small cans weigh 385 g.
Large cans weigh 200 g more.

Large cans weigh [   ] g.

4 Naomi is 71.
Rhoda is 23.

Naomi is [   ] years older.

5 87 story books.
48 topic books.

[   ] books altogether

6 Dan weighs 50 kg more than Ned.
Ned weighs 29 kg.

Dan weighs [   ] kg.

7 572 cars going north.
90 fewer going south.

[   ] cars going south

8 100 cm of string.
45 cm used.

[   ] cm left

9 314 people on a boat
90 get off.

[   ] people left

10 Lily has 40p more than Leo.
Leo has 35p.

Lily has [   ] p.

11 Ama's book has 124 pages.
Aisha's book has 36 fewer pages.

Aisha's book has [   ] pages.

12 200 toys in a shop.
130 are sold.

[   ] toys left

13 Todd has read 142 pages.
He reads another 60.

He has read [   ] pages.

14 81 children in Year 3.
29 in 3W. 26 in 3K.

[   ] children in 3F.

15 94 children on playground.
78 children join them.

[   ] children on playground

16 153 cars in car park.
85 leave.

[   ] cars left

```
Examples        3  7              1 4
            ×      8          4)5¹6
               2  9  6
                   5
```

Work out

1
```
   3  6
×     3
_____
```

2
```
   2  5
×     8
_____
```

3
```
   3  8
×     2
_____
```

4
```
   4  7
×     5
_____
```

5
```
   2  9
×     4
_____
```

6
```
   7  4
×     3
_____
```

7
```
   4  6
×     8
_____
```

8
```
   7  5
×     2
_____
```

9
```
   9  3
×     5
_____
```

10
```
   6  8
×     4
_____
```

11
```
   5  9
×     3
_____
```

12
```
   8  3
×     8
_____
```

Work out

13 4)6 8

14 3)7 5

15 5)9 5

16 2)6 8

17 8)1 0 4

18 4)9 6

19 3)5 7

20 5)8 0

21 2)9 2

22 8)1 2 0

23 4)7 2

24 3)8 1

Write the missing number in the box.

1 4 children at each table.

[ ] children at 7 tables.

2 24 sweets. 3 friends.

[ ] sweets each.

3 Jo has twelve 50p coins.

She has £ [ ] altogether.

4 Ten tickets cost £100.

One ticket costs £ [ ] .

5 Each box holds 8 cakes.

72 cakes [ ] boxes.

6 Pencils cost 20p each.
Pens cost 3 times as much.

Pens cost [ ] p each.

7 4 apples in each pack.

120 apples [ ] packs.

8 Eleven pairs of socks.

[ ] socks altogether.

9 [ ] 5p coins.
30p altogether.

10 Eight rubbers in each box.

50 boxes [ ] rubbers.

11 Groups of 3.

36 counters [ ] groups.

12 4 people in each tent.

9 tents [ ] people.

13 60 seconds in one minute.

[ ] seconds in two minutes.

14 480 g cake. 8 equal slices.

Each slice is [ ] g.

15 1000 ml of drink. 5 glasses.

[ ] ml in each glass.

16 40 cards in each box.
6 boxes.

[ ] cards.

17 4 pens cost 80p altogether.

Each pen costs [ ] p.

18 30 children in each class.

8 classes [ ] children.

19 Ava is half as old as Abbie.

Abbie is 70. Ava is [ ] .

20 5 chairs in each pile.

9 piles [ ] chairs.

1 How many minutes are there in one hour?   ....

2 How many hours are there in one day?   ....

How many minutes are left in the hour if the time is:

3 3:35   ....   7 4:42   ....   11 11:37   ....

4 7:20   ....   8 10:16   ....   12 8:01   ....

5 9:50   ....   9 2:53   ....   13 1:48   ....

6 6:05   ....   10 5:29   ....   14 12:14   ....

How many hours are left in the day if the time is:

15 7 pm   ....   19 11 am   ....   23 6 pm   ....

16 8 am   ....   20 9 pm   ....   24 1 am   ....

17 3 pm   ....   21 1 pm   ....   25 10 pm   ....

18 4 am   ....   22 6 am   ....   26 9 am   ....

27 A lesson starts at 9:20.
It ends at 10:15.

It lasts ⬚ minutes.

30 Nina gets on a train at 11:30.
She gets off at 12:07.

Her journey has taken ⬚ minutes.

28 A cake is put in the oven at 2:40.
It needs 30 minutes to bake.

It should be taken out at ⬚ .

31 A film finishes at 7:30.
It lasts 90 minutes.

It started at ⬚ .

29 Vince leaves a shop at 2:25.
He has been there for 25 minutes.

He went into the shop at ⬚ .

32 Perry leaves home at 5:25.
He is out for 50 minutes.

He returns at ⬚ .

Examples

$$1 = \frac{3}{8} + \frac{5}{8} = \frac{8}{8} \qquad \frac{3}{10} + \frac{2}{10} = \frac{5}{10} \qquad \frac{3}{5} - \frac{1}{5} = \frac{2}{5}$$

Fill in the box.
Use two colours to show each pair of fractions.

1 $1 = \frac{3}{4} + \frac{\square}{4}$

4 $1 = \frac{4}{10} + \frac{\square}{10}$

2 $1 = \frac{\square}{6} + \frac{3}{6}$

5 $1 = \frac{\square}{5} + \frac{3}{5}$

3 $1 = \frac{1}{3} + \frac{\square}{3}$

6 $1 = \frac{7}{8} + \frac{\square}{8}$

Fill in the box.

7 $\frac{1}{3} + \frac{1}{3} = \frac{\square}{3}$

8 $\frac{3}{8} + \frac{4}{8} = \frac{\square}{8}$

9 $\frac{3}{4} - \frac{1}{4} = \frac{\square}{4}$

10 $\frac{9}{10} - \frac{3}{10} = \frac{\square}{10}$

11 $\frac{1}{5} + \frac{2}{5} = \frac{\square}{5}$

12 $\frac{5}{12} + \frac{2}{12} = \frac{\square}{12}$

13 $\frac{7}{9} - \frac{4}{9} = \frac{\square}{9}$

14 $\frac{6}{7} - \frac{5}{7} = \frac{\square}{7}$

15 $\frac{4}{6} + \frac{\square}{6} = \frac{5}{6}$

16 $\frac{3}{10} + \frac{\square}{10} = \frac{8}{10}$

17 $\frac{4}{5} - \frac{\square}{5} = \frac{2}{5}$

18 $\frac{5}{8} - \frac{\square}{8} = \frac{1}{8}$

Examples

  $\frac{2}{3}$ is larger than $\frac{2}{5}$ $\frac{1}{3}$ is smaller than $\frac{2}{3}$

Draw a circle round the larger of each pair of fractions.

1 $\frac{2}{6}$ $\frac{1}{6}$ **4** $\frac{3}{7}$ $\frac{3}{10}$ **7** $\frac{4}{7}$ $\frac{3}{7}$

2 $\frac{1}{3}$ $\frac{1}{2}$ **5** $\frac{4}{8}$ $\frac{5}{8}$ **8** $\frac{2}{5}$ $\frac{2}{3}$

3 $\frac{5}{12}$ $\frac{7}{12}$ **6** $\frac{4}{5}$ $\frac{4}{9}$ **9** $\frac{1}{10}$ $\frac{9}{10}$

Write in order, smallest first.

10 $\frac{1}{2}$ $\frac{1}{4}$ $\frac{1}{10}$ $\frac{1}{\_}$ $\frac{1}{\_}$ $\frac{1}{\_}$ **13** $\frac{4}{12}$ $\frac{11}{12}$ $\frac{1}{12}$ — — —

11 $\frac{3}{5}$ $\frac{1}{5}$ $\frac{4}{5}$ — — —   **14** $\frac{2}{3}$ $\frac{2}{8}$ $\frac{2}{7}$ — — —

12 $\frac{5}{12}$ $\frac{5}{6}$ $\frac{5}{8}$ — — —   **15** $\frac{7}{9}$ $\frac{6}{9}$ $\frac{8}{9}$ — — —

Make two fractions smaller than the given fraction.

16 $\frac{3}{4}$ $\frac{3}{\square}$ $\frac{\square}{4}$ **19** $\frac{2}{3}$ $\frac{\square}{3}$ $\frac{2}{\square}$

17 $\frac{5}{7}$ $\frac{\square}{7}$ $\frac{5}{\square}$ **20** $\frac{4}{9}$ $\frac{4}{\square}$ $\frac{\square}{9}$

18 $\frac{7}{10}$ $\frac{7}{\square}$ $\frac{\square}{10}$ **21** $\frac{3}{6}$ $\frac{\square}{6}$ $\frac{3}{\square}$

Make two fractions larger than the given fraction.

22 $\frac{2}{5}$ $\frac{\square}{5}$ $\frac{2}{\square}$ **25** $\frac{5}{9}$ $\frac{\square}{9}$ $\frac{5}{\square}$

23 $\frac{3}{8}$ $\frac{3}{\square}$ $\frac{\square}{8}$ **26** $\frac{4}{10}$ $\frac{\square}{10}$ $\frac{4}{\square}$

24 $\frac{1}{7}$ $\frac{1}{\square}$ $\frac{\square}{7}$ **27** $\frac{6}{12}$ $\frac{6}{\square}$ $\frac{\square}{12}$

1 Use these words.
Label the shapes.

cone
cylinder
hemisphere
sphere

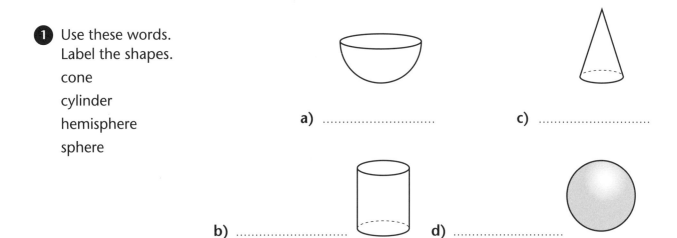

a) ....

b) ....

c) ....

d) ....

2 Complete the table for each of the polyhedra A–H shown below. Use these words.

cube   cuboid   octagonal prism   square based pyramid
pentagonal prism   triangular prism   triangular based pyramid

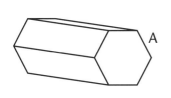

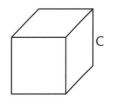
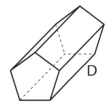

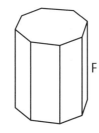
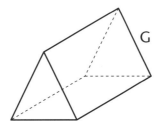
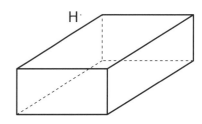

Letter	Shape	Faces	Edges	Vertices
A	hexagonal prism	8		
B				
C				
D				
E				
F				
G				
H				

Write right angle, acute or obtuse for each angle.

1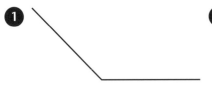

....

2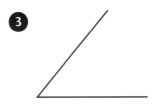

....

3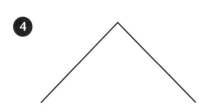

....

4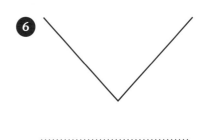

....

5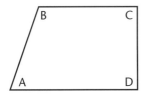

....

6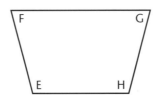

....

7 Write right angle, acute or obtuse for each angle A to L.

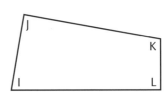

A   ....

B   ....

C   ....

D   ....

E   ....

F   ....

G   ....

H   ....

I   ....

J   ....

K   ....

L   ....

Write the answer in the box.

1 A T-shirt costs £9.
How much will two T-shirts cost?

£ ▢

2 Eight packets of crisps weigh 240 g altogether.
What does one packet weigh?

▢ g

3 Three 12 cm lengths are cut from a piece of string.
How much string has been cut off altogether?

▢ cm

4 A 600 ml tub of ice cream provides 10 equal servings.
How much ice cream is in each serving?

▢ ml

5 A new road will be 450 km long. One fifth has been built
How long is the road which has been built?

▢ km

6 A pie is cut into four equal slices Each slice is 70 g.
What is the weight of the pie?

▢ g

7 A full saucepan holds 1200 ml of water. It is one third full.
How much water is in the saucepan?

▢ ml

8 A running tap uses 8 litres of water every minute.
How much water is used if the tap is left running for 5 minutes?

▢ litres

9 Each book in a pile is 30 mm thick. There are ten books in the pile.
How tall is the pile in centimetres?

▢ cm

10 Four plane tickets cost £480 altogether.
What does each ticket cost?

£ ▢

11 Cans of dog food cost 60p each.
What do eight cans cost altogether?

£ ▢

12 Two sacks of potatoes have a total weight of 120 kg.
How much does one sack weigh?

▢ kg

Write these numbers in figures.

1 four hundred and fifty   ....

2 six hundred and seventy-two   ....

3 three hundred and eighty-four   ....

4 nine hundred and seven   ....

Write the missing number in each box.

5 $147 = 100 + \boxed{} + \boxed{7}$

6 $783 = \boxed{} + 80 + 3$

7 $529 = \boxed{} + 20 + \boxed{}$

8 $854 = 800 + \boxed{} + \boxed{}$

9 $638 = 600 + \boxed{}$

10 $215 \quad \boxed{} + 5$

11 $962 \quad 900 + \boxed{}$

12 $306 \quad \boxed{} + 6$

Work out

13 $704 + 10$ ....

14 $293 + 10$ ....

15 $978 - 10$ ....

16 $602 - 10$ ....

17 $526 + 100$ ....

18 $857 + 100$ ....

19 $463 - 100$ ....

20 $185 - 100$ ....

Circle the larger number.

21   699   701

22   387   378

23   502   520

24   854   845

Start at 0. Count on

25 six steps of 4   ....

26 five steps of 8   ....

27 four steps of 50   ....

28 nine steps of 4   ....

29 eight steps of 8   ....

30 seven steps of 50   ....

Count on

31 6 from 147   ....

32 8 from 423   ....

33 40 from 786   ....

34 70 from 572   ....

35 300 from 639   ....

36 500 from 295   ....

Work out

1 $185 + 7$ ....

2 $327 + 9$ ....

3 $762 + 40$ ....

4 $958 + 80$ ....

5 $491 + 50$ ....

6 $874 + 60$ ....

7 $516 + 300$ ....

8 $240 + 500$ ....

9 $673 - 5$ ....

10 $391 - 8$ ....

11 $728 - 30$ ....

12 $245 - 70$ ....

13 $504 - 60$ ....

14 $159 - 90$ ....

15 $982 - 600$ ....

16 $436 - 400$ ....

17 $47 + 34$ ....

18 $65 + 29$ ....

19 $76 + 56$ ....

20 $89 + 34$ ....

21 $92 + 68$ ....

22 $68 + 47$ ....

23 $76 + 75$ ....

24 $97 + 36$ ....

25 $72 - 47$ ....

26 $96 - 39$ ....

27 $100 - 54$ ....

28 $100 - 81$ ....

29 $133 - 98$ ....

30 $114 - 36$ ....

31 $141 - 77$ ....

32 $105 - 46$ ....

33 6×2 ....

34 11×3 ....

35 9×4 ....

36 5×8 ....

37 120×5 ....

38 70×3 ....

39 60×4 ....

40 90×8 ....

41 $16 \div 2$ ....

42 $27 \div 3$ ....

43 $48 \div 4$ ....

44 $64 \div 8$ ....

45 $450 \div 5$ ....

46 $360 \div 3$ ....

47 $280 \div 4$ ....

48 $480 \div 8$ ....

Write the missing numbers.

49 $693 + \boxed{} = 708$

50 $284 + \boxed{} = 344$

51 $\boxed{} + 5 = 243$

52 $\boxed{} + 90 = 535$

53 $132 - \boxed{} = 47$

54 $160 - \boxed{} = 91$

55 $\boxed{} - 63 = 78$

56 $\boxed{} - 57 = 67$

57 $\boxed{} \times 5 = 350$

58 $\boxed{} \times 4 = 440$

59 $\boxed{} \div 3 = 80$

60 $\boxed{} \div 8 = 70$

Examples

$$\begin{array}{r} 4\ 9\ 6 \\ +\ 3\ 2\ 7 \\ \hline 8\ 2\ 3 \\ {\scriptstyle 1\ 1} \end{array}$$

$$\begin{array}{r} {\scriptstyle 6\ 1} \\ \not{7}\ 3\ 5 \\ -\ 2\ 8\ 2 \\ \hline 4\ 5\ 3 \end{array}$$

$$\begin{array}{r} 6\ 3 \\ \times\quad\ \ 8 \\ \hline 5\ 0\ 4 \\ {\scriptstyle 2} \end{array}$$

$$3\overline{)5^2\ 7} \quad \begin{array}{r} 1\ 9 \end{array}$$

Work out

1
$$\begin{array}{r} 3\ 3\ 7 \\ +\ 1\ 2\ 5 \\ \hline \end{array}$$

7
$$\begin{array}{r} 7\ 8\ 4 \\ -\ 4\ 1\ 5 \\ \hline \end{array}$$

13
$$\begin{array}{r} 7\ 6 \\ \times\quad\ \ 3 \\ \hline \end{array}$$

19
$$2\overline{)5\ 2}$$

2
$$\begin{array}{r} 5\ 6\ 4 \\ +\ 3\ 5\ 6 \\ \hline \end{array}$$

8
$$\begin{array}{r} 5\ 3\ 6 \\ -\ 1\ 7\ 2 \\ \hline \end{array}$$

14
$$\begin{array}{r} 4\ 5 \\ \times\quad\ \ 4 \\ \hline \end{array}$$

20
$$3\overline{)7\ 2}$$

3
$$\begin{array}{r} 2\ 8\ 9 \\ +\ 2\ 7\ 8 \\ \hline \end{array}$$

9
$$\begin{array}{r} 9\ 0\ 7 \\ -\ 2\ 3\ 6 \\ \hline \end{array}$$

15
$$\begin{array}{r} 2\ 7 \\ \times\quad\ \ 8 \\ \hline \end{array}$$

21
$$4\overline{)6\ 0}$$

4
$$\begin{array}{r} 6\ 4\ 6 \\ +\ 1\ 9\ 8 \\ \hline \end{array}$$

10
$$\begin{array}{r} 4\ 9\ 5 \\ -\ 3\ 6\ 7 \\ \hline \end{array}$$

16
$$\begin{array}{r} 9\ 6 \\ \times\quad\ \ 5 \\ \hline \end{array}$$

22
$$5\overline{)8\ 5}$$

5
$$\begin{array}{r} 4\ 7\ 5 \\ +\ 2\ 3\ 5 \\ \hline \end{array}$$

11
$$\begin{array}{r} 8\ 1\ 8 \\ -\ 5\ 9\ 3 \\ \hline \end{array}$$

17
$$\begin{array}{r} 3\ 9 \\ \times\quad\ \ 3 \\ \hline \end{array}$$

23
$$2\overline{)7\ 8}$$

6
$$\begin{array}{r} 3\ 9\ 8 \\ +\ 2\ 5\ 4 \\ \hline \end{array}$$

12
$$\begin{array}{r} 6\ 4\ 2 \\ -\ 1\ 2\ 8 \\ \hline \end{array}$$

18
$$\begin{array}{r} 6\ 8 \\ \times\quad\ \ 4 \\ \hline \end{array}$$

24
$$5\overline{)7\ 0}$$

Write the fraction shown.

1
$$0 \quad A \qquad\qquad B \quad 1$$

$A = \dfrac{\square}{\square}$

$B = \dfrac{\square}{\square}$

2
$$0 \quad C \qquad D \qquad 1$$

$C = \dfrac{\square}{\square}$

$D = \dfrac{\square}{\square}$

Complete the equivalent fractions.

3
$\dfrac{1}{\square}$ $\dfrac{2}{\square}$

4
$\dfrac{\square}{6}$ $\dfrac{\square}{3}$

Circle the larger fraction.

5 $\dfrac{3}{6}$ $\dfrac{4}{6}$

6 $\dfrac{2}{3}$ $\dfrac{2}{5}$

7 $\dfrac{3}{8}$ $\dfrac{7}{8}$

8 $\dfrac{5}{9}$ $\dfrac{5}{12}$

Write in order, smallest first

9 $\dfrac{1}{3}$ $\dfrac{1}{8}$ $\dfrac{1}{5}$ ....

10 $\dfrac{4}{7}$ $\dfrac{6}{7}$ $\dfrac{3}{7}$ ....

Fill in the boxes

11 $1 = \dfrac{3}{10} + \dfrac{\square}{10}$

12 $1 = \dfrac{\square}{6} + \dfrac{5}{6}$

13 $\dfrac{1}{5} + \dfrac{2}{5} = \dfrac{\square}{\square}$

14 $\dfrac{7}{9} - \dfrac{4}{9} = \dfrac{\square}{\square}$

15 $\dfrac{3}{8} + \dfrac{2}{8} = \dfrac{\square}{\square}$

16 $\dfrac{11}{12} - \dfrac{5}{12} = \dfrac{\square}{\square}$

17 Count on 4 tenths from $\dfrac{2}{10}$ ....

18 Count back 3 tenths from $\dfrac{8}{10}$ ....

19 Count on 6 tenths from $\dfrac{1}{10}$ ....

20 Count back 5 tenths from 1 ....

Work out

21 $\dfrac{1}{5}$ of 40 ....

22 $\dfrac{1}{4}$ of 24 ....

23 $\dfrac{1}{3}$ of 21 ....

24 $\dfrac{1}{10}$ of 100 ....

25 $\dfrac{1}{2}$ of 18 ....

26 $\dfrac{1}{8}$ of 16 ....

27 $\dfrac{1}{5}$ of 60 ....

28 $\dfrac{1}{4}$ of 32 ....

29 $\dfrac{1}{3}$ of 15 ....

30 $\dfrac{1}{10}$ of 70 ....

31 $\dfrac{1}{2}$ of 24 ....

32 $\dfrac{1}{8}$ of 48 ....

Write the answer in the box.

1 4 cm = ☐ mm

2 2 m = ☐ cm

3 5 km = ☐ m

4 8 litres = ☐ ml

5 3 kg = ☐ g

6 $1\frac{1}{2}$ hours = ☐ minutes

7 27 mm = ☐ cm ☐ mm

8 540 cm = ☐ m ☐ cm

9 700 m = ☐ km ☐ m

10 4800 ml = ☐ litres ☐ ml

11 2500 g = ☐ kg ☐ g

12 300 seconds = ☐ minutes

Write the measurements in the box.

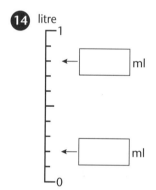

13 kg
2 — ← ☐ g
1 — ← ☐ g
0 —

14 litre
1 — ← ☐ ml
← ☐ ml
0 —

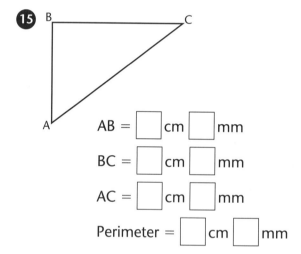

15
AB = ☐ cm ☐ mm

BC = ☐ cm ☐ mm

AC = ☐ cm ☐ mm

Perimeter = ☐ cm ☐ mm

Write each time in figures, using am and pm.

16 10 to 3, afternoon ....

17 25 past 4, night ....

18 7 minutes past midnight ....

19 20 to 6, evening ....

20 How long is each lesson?

	PE	Science
Start	10:40	1:15
Finish	11:25	2:10
Length (mins)	☐	☐

21 Work out the total cost of buying these items and the change from £2.

pencil 25p
rubber 40p
ruler 79p

Cost £ ☐   Change ☐ p

Write the answer in the box.

1. The sum of 75 and 48 is [ ] .

2. Three and a half litres is [ ] ml.

3. Nisha has seven 50p coins. She has £[ ] altogether.

4. Write four hundred and three in figures. [ ]

5. 65 cm is cut off a one metre length of wood. [ ] cm is left.

6. Five eighths of a cake is eaten. What fraction is left? [ ] eighths.

7. Four people sit at each table. [ ] tables are needed for 48 people.

8. It is 2:57. It is [ ] minutes until quarter to four.

9. 82 is 46 larger than [ ] .

10. A square based pyramid has [ ] faces and [ ] edges.

11. Eighty pins in one packet. [ ] pins in three packets.

12. Two hundred seconds is [ ] minutes [ ] seconds.

13. Jack has £114. He spends £29. He has £[ ] left.

14. One eighth of 72 is [ ] .

15. The nine in 495 has a value of [ ] .

16. Eleven multiplied by 4 is [ ] .

17. [ ] is 60 more than 287.

18. Laura spends £2·70. She pays £5. She is given £[ ] change.

19. Half of 140 is [ ] .

20. A square has sides of 3 cm 5 mm. Its perimeter is [ ] cm.